BOBBS-MERRILL

Best of Children's Literature

The books in this series are:

SUNNY AND GAY

FOOLISH AND WISE

FUN ALL AROUND

SHINING HOURS

TIME FOR ADVENTURE

BEYOND THE HORIZON

LIBRARY OF CONGRESS CATALOG CARD NUMBER: 60-12936

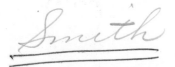

FOOLISH AND WISE

FOOLISH AND WISE

BOBBS-MERRILL
Best of Children's Literature

Compilers and Editors

NILA BANTON SMITH
Director, Reading Institute
New York University

HAZEL C. HART
Assistant Professor of Education
Butler University

CLARA BELLE BAKER
Former Director, Children's School
National College of Education

THE **BOBBS-MERRILL** COMPANY, INC.
A SUBSIDIARY OF HOWARD W. SAMS & CO., INC.
Publishers • INDIANAPOLIS • NEW YORK

FOOLISH AND WISE

CONTENTS

ANIMAL LAND

NEIGHBORS AND FRIENDS

WHEELS AND WINGS

MOSTLY NONSENSE

HAPPY HOLIDAYS

FUN AND FANCY

ANIMAL LAND

YA-HOO FOR PANCHO

Ned was a very little cowboy, who had
a very little horse. His little horse was
a black and white pony named Pancho.

Pancho was a good pony, but a funny one.
There was something that he would not do.
He would not run. He would not run
at all. He just walked!

8

One morning Ned ran out of the house
with Pancho's saddle.

"Today is a big day," he said to Pancho.
"We are going to the rodeo!"

Pancho put his head away up in the air
and went, "Whe-e-e-e-e."

Ned laughed as he put the saddle
on Pancho's back. He could see that
Pancho wanted to go to the rodeo, too.

"All the cowboys will go to town today,"
Ned said. "They will ride in the rodeo.
The fastest horse will get a new saddle.
You could be the fastest one of all.
Please, please run, Pancho."

Pancho just put his head away down.
He walked all the way to town.

"We want to go to the rodeo ring,"
said Ned as he and his pony came to town.
"Please, please run, Pancho."

Pancho walked on. He did not run.

"Please run, Pancho," said Ned again.
"Soon the cowboys will ride their horses
all around the rodeo ring. They will go
ya-hoo and ride very fast."

Pancho walked all the way to the ring,
with his head away down.

As Ned and Pancho came to the ring, something made a noise. Bang! Bang! The noise was right under Pancho's feet. He jumped and began to run.

"Stop, Pancho, stop!" called Ned. "I cannot stay in the saddle when you run so fast."

Pancho would not stop. He just went faster and faster and faster. He ran around the big rodeo ring three times. Then he stopped.

Ned sat there on Pancho's back, tired
out from his fast ride. Soon a man came
over with a new saddle in his hands.

"My boy," he said to Ned. "You are
a good cowboy, and you have a good pony.
No other pony could run as fast as he did,
so this saddle is for you."

Ned was so surprised and so tired that
all he said was, "Thank you."

Pancho was not tired. He put his head
back and went, "Whe-e-e-e-e!"

Then all the cowboys laughed and called,
"Ya-hoo! Ya-hoo for Pancho!"

ELFRED GETS BUSY

It was opening night at the circus,
and all of the circus animals were busy.
That is, all of them were busy but Elfred.
Elfred was not doing a thing.
This was strange, too, for Elfred was
a very big elephant.

Elfred wanted to be like other animals
in the circus. He wanted to do tricks
in the ring, but no one would let him.
When he did tricks, he broke things.

When Elfred put his front feet on a box,
he broke it. When he tried to stay up
on his back feet, he came down so hard
that he moved everything around him.
Elfred was just too big!

He had no way of knowing that tonight
he would get busy. He would get as busy
as one elephant could be.

About this time a policeman jumped
into his car and started for the circus.
He made his car go very fast, for he wanted
to be on time. He had to be at the circus
to look after things.

On his way there, it started to rain hard.
"Jumping jack rabbits!" said the policeman.
"It is raining cats and dogs. I cannot see
where I am going."

Soon the car went squ-i-i-shh, plop!
It plopped into the mud beside the road.
The police car was stopped by the mud.

The policeman had to call for some help
over his police car radio.

"Send a big truck," he radioed. "My car is
off the road in the mud."

Soon a big blue truck came down the road.
It came down the road fast in the rain.

"Jumping jack rabbits!" said the driver.
"It is raining cats and dogs. I cannot see
the road in front of me."

There was another squ-i-i-shh, plop!
The big blue truck plopped into the mud
beside the police car.

Now the policeman called for help again over his radio. This time a big red truck came down the road from the city. It came as fast as it could in the rain.

Squi-i-shh, plop! Yes, you guessed right. The big red truck was stuck in the mud! Now the policeman's car and the two trucks were all stuck in the mud.

"Send another truck! Send it fast!" the policeman called again on his radio. "All three of us are stuck in the mud now, the two big trucks and my car."

"We have no other trucks right now,"
the call came back. "They are all busy
in the city getting cars out of the mud."

"Then please call the circus people for me
at once," the policeman said. "Tell them
that I am stuck in the mud."

Time went on, and the rain came down.
It rained more and more and more.
The three men sat in the policeman's car,
wishing that they were home in their beds.
It would be good to be home in bed.

All at once one of the men cried out,
"Look up ahead. What is that?"

"Jumping jack rabbits!" another one said.
"Now it is raining elephants!"

It was not raining elephants at all.
It was just raining Elfred! That is,
Elfred was walking down the road.
The circus people had asked him to get
the cars out of the mud.

Elfred did not go squ-i-i-shh, plop,
into the mud beside the road. He began
to push. Then he began to pull.

Then he pushed and pulled some more.
He was not too big for this work. Soon
he had the two trucks and the police car
back on the road again.

So that night Elfred was very busy.
He was as busy as one elephant could be.

21

MY DOG

My dog listens when I talk.

He goes with me for a walk.

When I sleep, he's sleepy too.

He does everything I do.

He has eyes that always show

He knows everything I know.

I never do a thing but he

Thinks it is all right for me.

When I speak, he always minds.

He shares with me the things he finds.

When other people say I'm bad,

He hangs his head and looks so sad.

He cuddles up and laps my hand

And tells me he can understand.

MR. JACKSON, MAILMAN

Mr. Jackson ran fast down the sidewalk to the mailbox. He stopped and went sniff, sniff, sniff with his nose. Then he looked up and down the street. No one was there, so Mr. Jackson sat down.

You may think it was strange that he sat down right on the sidewalk, but it was not strange at all. This Mr. Jackson was a dog. He was not big, but he was long. He looked something like a long hot dog.

Every morning Mr. Jackson ran down
to this mailbox and met the mailman.
The mailman came here to get letters
and other mail stored in the mailbox.
He put the mail into his mailbag.

After Mr. Jackson and the mailman met,
they walked down the street together.
Together they went to houses and stores
with mail for many people.

This morning Mr. Jackson knew that
something was not right. He had not met
the mailman, but he knew from sniffing
that the mailman had been there.

So he sat there in front of the mailbox,
thinking what to do next. He sniffed
once more. Yes, the mailman had been
there, but not very long ago.

Then Mr. Jackson saw something little
away back under the mailbox. He saw
a little white box.

Mr. Jackson's nose went sniff, sniff, sniff, all around the little white box. Yes, it had been in the mailman's hands. He took the box in his mouth and pulled it out from under the mailbox.

Now Mr. Jackson knew what to do next. "The mailman must have lost this box, so I'll take it to him," he thought. "I'll go as fast as I can."

Off he went, with the box in his mouth.

Mr. Jackson soon turned into a street
with stores on it. He liked this street,
for he had a friend in every store.

His friend from the pet store met him
at the door. "Hello, Mr. J.," he said.
"You look hot and a little tired. Here is
a drink of cold water for you."

Mr. J. did not drink the cold water that
the pet store man put down on the floor.
He just sniffed all around and thought,
"Yes, the mailman has been here."

"How are things today?" asked the man
at the candy store when Mr. J. stopped
there. "Do you want some candy?"

Mr. J. did want some candy very much,
just as he had wanted a drink of water.
Then he thought about the mailman again,
and he did not want them so much.

He sniffed and sniffed around the floor and
thought, "Yes, the mailman has been here
ahead of me, too. I must run much faster
to catch up with him."

Soon Mr. J. came to a busy street corner.
There was a stop light at this busy corner,
and he had to wait for a long time.

He waited and waited, with the little box
in his mouth. "My, oh, my!" he thought.
"How can I go fast when I have to wait
for so many cars to go by?"

Around another corner, Mr. Jackson saw
something that made him wag his tail.
There was the mailman! He was coming out
of a big store.

Mr. J. ran up to him, wagging his tail
every step of the way.

"Hello, Mr. Jackson," said the mailman.
"I could not wait for you, but I thought
you would catch up with me."

Mr. J. gave the little box to the mailman
and wagged his tail some more.

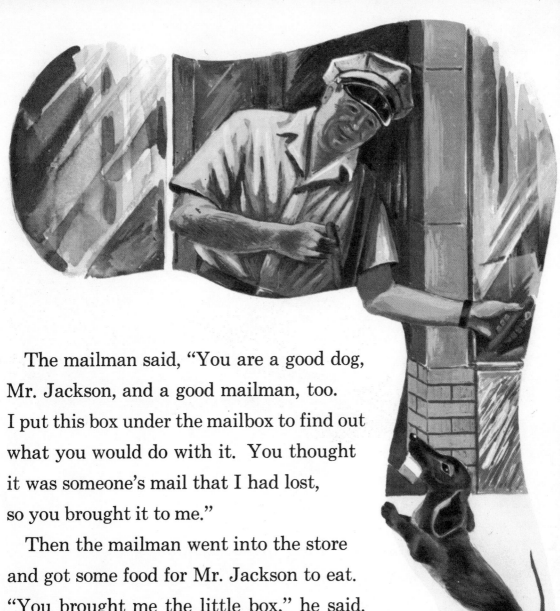

The mailman said, "You are a good dog,
Mr. Jackson, and a good mailman, too.
I put this box under the mailbox to find out
what you would do with it. You thought
it was someone's mail that I had lost,
so you brought it to me."

Then the mailman went into the store
and got some food for Mr. Jackson to eat.
"You brought me the little box," he said.
"So here is something you like."

Mr. J. sniffed and wagged his tail faster
and faster. Why, hot dogs were the food
he liked best of all!

A LITTLE BEAR TAKES A WALK

There once was a little bear that lived
in the big woods. He lived with his mother
in a cave in the side of a hill.

The little bear liked his home in the cave,
but he did not think much about it. He was
far too busy sleeping. He wanted to sleep
about all the time.

One day his mother said, "Little bear, come with me. It is time for you to see what the world is like outside our cave. You must learn the ways of the woods and how to live in the woods."

"World outside? Ways of the woods?" thought the little bear. "What are they? I think I'll just stay here and sleep."

Then the little bear's mother pushed him right out of the cave—ker-plunk!

The little bear got up and looked around in surprise. This was a very strange world to him, but he soon began to like it.

There was a sun to help him stay warm and to help him see where he was going. There was a big woods where he could run and play all day long. Yes, he was pleased with everything around him.

Soon he became warm playing in the sun, and he wanted to sleep. Then he lay down beside a big tree in the woods and forgot all about the outside world.

What do you think the mother bear did when she saw the little bear sleeping? She came and tried to make him get up, but he would not move. Then she rolled him over and over down a hill. This was her way of taking care of him.

Just what did the mother bear want?
She wanted the little bear to keep moving
about in the outside world. She wanted
him to do things and to learn to take care
of himself. She did not want him to sleep.

From then on the little bear tried hard
to keep from going to sleep again.

The mother bear began to sniff and took
the little bear to a big open place where
there were good red berries to eat.

The little bear began to sniff, too,
but he didn't know why he was sniffing.
He just knew that he sniffed something
good to eat there in the sun.

The mother bear showed the little bear
how to get some of the red berries. Once
he began to eat, she did not have to show
him again. "Yum! Yum!" he thought.

Soon a rabbit jumped out in front of him
and, PLOP, the little bear sat right down.

Then what do you think he did? He just
sat there and went on eating berries.

36

Next the mother bear took the little bear down to a river. She wanted him to learn something about water.

Soon after she came to the river, she put her paw in the water and pulled out a fish for the little bear.

The little bear ate the fish and thought, "Now I'll get a fish, too."

He put out his paw and, SPLASH, he went right into the water. Then he had to splash some more to get out of the water.

The little bear did not catch a fish, but he learned something about water.

The mother bear took the little bear back
to the woods. She wanted him to learn
how to climb trees.

When she found a good tree, she put
her paws on the tree and climbed up a way
to show the little bear what to do. Then
she came back down.

The little bear did not want to learn
to climb. He was afraid and just waited
with his paws on the tree. His mother had
to push him to make him go up.

When he got up in the tree, he was afraid
to come down. Then his mother had to
climb up and show him how to come down.

38

Soon the little bear was climbing trees
all around the woods.

There was a hole in one of the trees where
honeybees lived. The honeybees had stored
honey in the hole.

When the little bear came to this tree,
he sniffed the honey. "There is something
good up there," he thought. "I'll climb up
to find out what it is."

He climbed up and put one of his paws
in the hole. Then the bees began to go
"Z-z-z" all around his head.

Down he came fast, with the bees coming
after him. Then what do you think he did?
He ran as fast as he could to the cave,
and he did not show up again that day.

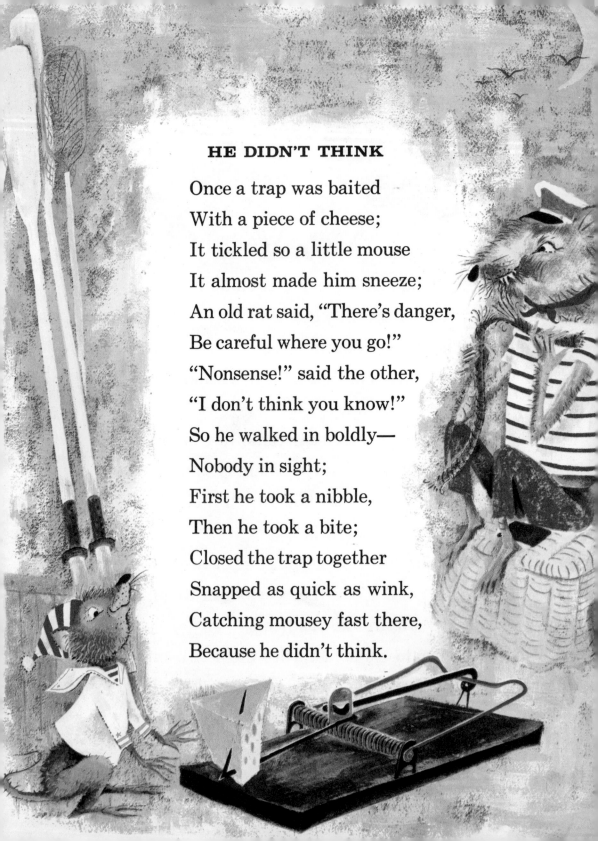

HE DIDN'T THINK

Once a trap was baited
With a piece of cheese;
It tickled so a little mouse
It almost made him sneeze;
An old rat said, "There's danger,
Be careful where you go!"
"Nonsense!" said the other,
"I don't think you know!"
So he walked in boldly—
Nobody in sight;
First he took a nibble,
Then he took a bite;
Closed the trap together
Snapped as quick as wink,
Catching mousey fast there,
Because he didn't think.

NEIGHBORS AND
FRIENDS

A FISH STORY

Kenny was very cross. He was so cross
that he did not want to laugh or play.
Kenny's father and his big brother Jim
were going fishing without Kenny.

"Please let me go," Kenny said.

"No, not this time," said his father.
Then his father and his brother Jim got
into the car and went away.

"You can go along next time, Kenny boy,"
his father called.

"Now, Kenny," his mother said as he came banging into the house. "You can have fun with your toys, or you can go fishing yourself. Why not ask Andy to go fishing with you at Raccoon Pond?"

"Raccoon Pond!" said Kenny. "Who wants to go to that old place? I would like to go fishing at some new place."

"Please go, Kenny," his mother went on.
"You can have fun at Raccoon Pond."

"No——" Kenny began. Then he stopped.
The more he thought about it, the more
he thought that Raccoon Pond might be
a good place to go, after all.

He and Andy might catch a lot of fish
at Raccoon Pond. They might catch more
than his father and Jim. It would be fun
to do something like that.

After a while, Kenny took his fish pole
and walked to Andy's house. All the way
he thought what fun it would be to catch
more fish than his father and Jim.

"Will I go fishing at Raccoon Pond!"
said Andy when Kenny asked him. "Well,
you just wait while I get my pole!"

Andy had not lived on a farm very long.
To him, everything about a farm was new
and lots of fun.

"Remember one thing," Kenny said as
they walked to the pond.

"Well, what is it?" said Andy.

"Remember not to talk while we fish."

"Why?" asked Andy.

"We cannot talk because we must catch
a lot of fish today," Kenny said.

"Why?" Andy asked again.

"Just because!" Kenny said.

When the boys came to Raccoon Pond,
they began to fish right away.

Andy soon tired of not talking at all, and he asked in a quiet voice, "Why is this place called Raccoon Pond?"

Kenny's voice was quiet, too. He said, "Because there are many raccoons around here. They come to this pond to fish."

"They do?" Andy said, forgetting to be quiet. "Have you seen a raccoon?"

"Sh! Yes, I have seen one," said Kenny. "One got inside our house a while ago, and we had a hard time getting it out."

Then Kenny forgot about being quiet, for he thought that something was pulling his fish pole into the water.

"I have caught a fish!" Kenny cried.

"Pull it in! Pull it in!" said Andy.

Kenny pulled and pulled on his pole
until he thought that he could not pull
any more. Then the fish pole came up,
and Kenny went down—on his back.

Andy looked at what Kenny had caught.
"What is that thing, anyway?" he asked.

"Well, what do you know!" said Kenny
when he saw what he had caught. "Wait
until my mother sees this!"

"Mother! Father! Jim!" called Kenny as he ran into the house. "Come and see what I caught in Raccoon Pond!"

"No!" said his father.

"Well, that IS something," said Jim.

Kenny's mother took one look and cried, "Oh, you found my gold bracelet!"

"When that raccoon got into our house, he must have run off with the bracelet," said Kenny's father.

"Anyone can catch a fish when he goes fishing," said Kenny's mother. "It took Kenny to pull in my gold bracelet."

49

THE SECRET

We have a secret, just we three,
The robin, and I, and the sweet cherry
    tree;
The bird told the tree, and the tree told
    me,
And nobody knows it but just us three.

But of course the robin knows it best,
Because he built the—I shan't tell the rest;
And laid the four little—something in it—
I'm afraid I shall tell it every minute.

But if the tree and the robin don't peep,
I'll try my best the secret to keep;
Though I know when the little birds fly
    about
Then the whole secret will be out.

MR. PICKLE'S SURPRISE

Mr. Pickle had worked as the janitor
at Hillside School for a very long time.
Every day, for as long as the children
could remember, Mr. Pickle had met them
with a happy "Good morning."

The janitor liked all of the children,
and the children liked him. He was more
than just a janitor. He was a good friend
of every boy and girl in the school.

One day after school Mr. Pickle went
into one of the rooms to do his work.
As he looked around the room, he saw
a colored paper under a chair.

When he pulled the colored paper out
from under the chair, he took a look at it.
This is what he saw—

"A birthday party," Mr. Pickle said
to himself, and the thought of it made
him very happy. The children asked him
to every birthday party, so he thought
that they would ask him to this one.

He looked at the colored paper again.
"That is strange," he said to himself.
"There is nothing here that says when
or where the party will be."

He went on with his work. "Oh, well,"
he thought. "The children will tell me
about the party tomorrow."

All the next day Mr. Pickle waited and waited for the children to say something about the birthday party.

All day long nothing was said about it, and Mr. Pickle was a little sad. "Oh, well," he thought again. "I will find out about the party tomorrow."

Tomorrow came, but nothing happened. By the time school was over for the day, Mr. Pickle was very sad.

"There just is not going to be a party, after all," he said to himself.

The next day Mr. Pickle was surprised when he saw the children, but he said, "Good morning," as he did every day.

"Something is happening," he thought. "The girls are wearing their best dresses, and the boys have washed their faces."

He was right. The girls were wearing their best dresses. The boys had washed their faces. Something was happening.

Mr. Pickle was sad, because he thought he knew what was happening. "I was right about that party," he said to himself. "The children are having a birthday party, but they did not want me to come."

He was too sad to do his work. He went to his room and sat down on a big chair. "I have been asked to every birthday party before," he thought. "Why not this one?"

Before long, a little boy came hurrying
to the janitor's room.

"Mr. Pickle, Mr. Pickle," he called.
"Come to our room at once! Someone broke
a window. Please hurry!"

Mr. Pickle did not say anything. He did
not care about the window. He did not want
to fix it. He did not want to fix anything.
He did not want to hurry.

Very slowly he got up from his chair.
Then he walked to the schoolroom slowly,
and slowly opened the door.

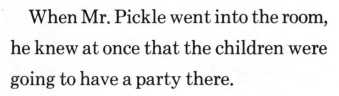

When Mr. Pickle went into the room, he knew at once that the children were going to have a party there.

"It is going to be a wonderful party, but I was not asked to it," he thought. "I might as well fix the window."

Just then the children began to sing, "Happy Birthday to You."

Mr. Pickle looked all around the room to find out who was having a birthday, but he could not tell.

It was not until he heard the children
sing, "Happy Birthday, Mr. Pickle," that
he remembered today was HIS birthday.

Mr. Pickle smiled a big, happy smile.
"What do you know about that!" he said.
"I thought you did not want me to come
to your party, but the party is for me.
You were just keeping it for a surprise,
and a wonderful surprise it is, too!"

LOCKED IN THE SUPERMARKET

Bonnie lived on a street where there was a big supermarket, She liked to go there because Mr. Wells, who ran the store, had a cat with three baby kittens.

One day after school Bonnie found one of the kittens by her house. "Oh, Kitty," she said. "I must take you right back to your mother."

It was almost time for Mr. Wells to lock the supermarket, so she must hurry.

Bonnie picked up the kitten and ran fast
to the supermarket. It was almost dark,
but people were still picking out things
here and there in the store.

"Do not cry," said Bonnie to the kitten.
"You will soon see your mother again."

"Meow, meow, meow," said the kitten.

Bonnie went to a box in a dark corner
of the store. There she found the mother cat
with her other kittens.

"Look here," she cried. "I have brought
one of your kittens back to you."

"Meow, meow," went the mother cat.

"Now be good," Bonnie said as she put
the kitten in the box. "Don't run away
again without telling your mother. Don't
come to my house again."

Bonnie sat down on the floor to play
with the kittens. "I shall play with them
for just a little while," she thought.
"Then I shall go home to eat."

Once Bonnie began to play, she forgot
about going home. At last she jumped up.
The supermarket was quiet, for there were
no people in the store.

Bonnie ran fast to the big front door,
but found that it was locked. She pulled
and pulled, but she could not open it.

"Mr. Wells! Mr. Wells!" she called.
"Come to help me! I can't get out!"

Mr. Wells did not come. There was not
a sound in the store.

"He must not hear me," thought Bonnie,
so she called again. "Mr. Wells, can you
hear me? I can't get out."

Still there was no sound in the store.
By now Bonnie knew that she was locked
in the supermarket all by herself.

"Oh, what shall I do?" she cried. "What
shall I do?"

For a time Bonnie waited inside the door
and thought. She was afraid to walk around
in the dark supermarket alone. If only
someone would come to get her!

Soon the mother cat came from the back
of the store and lay down at Bonnie's feet.
"I am just like your kitten," Bonnie said
to the cat. "I did not remember to tell
my mother where I was going."

When Bonnie thought about her mother,
she almost cried. "I must let her know
that I am here alone," she said.

Then she saw the telephone. "Oh, good!"
she cried. "There is a telephone."

Bonnie did not know how to call a number
by herself. At school she had learned that
the number "O" would get the operator.
She found this number and called it.

"May I help you?" said the operator.

"Yes, my name is Bonnie Black and I live
on Garden Street," she told the operator.
"Please call my mother and tell her that
I am locked in Mr. Wells's supermarket
not far from our house."

64

After Bonnie talked with the operator,
she didn't want to wait. She was ready
to go right away.

When no one came right away, she thought
something was wrong. Had the operator told
her mother the wrong store?

By now she was almost ready to cry. Then
all at once she saw Mr. Wells at the door.
Back of him were her father and mother.

Soon Bonnie was home and everyone was
happy. "That kitten went away from home
and didn't tell anyone, and I know a girl
who did that, too," said her mother.

THE ICE-CREAM MAN

When summer's in the city,
   And brick's a blaze of heat,
The Ice-cream Man with his little cart
   Goes trundling down the street.

Beneath his round umbrella,
   Oh, what a joyful sight,
To see him fill the cones with mounds
   Of cooling brown or white:

Vanilla, chocolate, strawberry,
   Or chilly things to drink
From bottles full of frosty-fizz,
   Green, orange, white, or pink.

His cart might be a flower bed
   Of roses and sweet peas,
The way the children cluster round
   As thick as honeybees.

From *Taxis and Toadstools* by Rachel Field. Copyright 1926 by Doubleday & Company, Inc, Reprinted by permission of the publishers.

JUST A MINUTE

One day when Jim came into the house, he smelled something good. He said, "Oh, what smells so good?"

His mother said that she was getting dinner. That was what smelled so good.

"Will dinner be ready soon?" asked Jim.

"In just a minute," his mother said.

Jim wanted to know what a minute was, but his mother was too busy to tell him. He went into the living room and looked at a big book until dinner was ready.

67

"I know what a minute is," said Jim
when his mother called him to dinner.
"A minute is a big book."

"You are a funny boy," said his mother.

After dinner Jim asked his father
to tell him a story.

"In just a minute," his father said.
"Right now I want to take a short rest."

His father lay down for a short rest,
and Jim turned on the radio.

Jim listened to a man singing songs
on the radio. He was still listening when
his father got up after his short rest.

"Now I am ready to tell you that story,
Jim," said his father.

"Father," said Jim. "I know now what
a minute really is. It is a man singing
five songs on the radio."

Father laughed and began the story.
It was a good story, and Jim liked it.

Before long Mother said it was getting
late and Jim would have to go to bed.

"Right away?" asked Jim.

"In just a minute," Mother answered.

Jim hoped that this minute was going
to be a long one, but it was a short one.
Almost as soon as he took his toys out
of the box, Mother said, "It really is
late now, Jim. You must go to bed."

"Now I know what a minute is," said Jim.
"It is taking all my toys out of the box,
but not having time to play with them."

Jim didn't go right to sleep. He lay
there in bed and thought, "A minute is
such a funny thing. Sometimes it is this,
and sometimes it is that."

In the living room Jim's mother said
to his father, "I hope nothing is wrong
with Jim. He said such strange things
today about what a minute is."

Father laughed and said, "Nothing is
wrong. He wants to know what a minute is,
but so far he has not found the answer.
I will show him tomorrow."

Breakfast was ready when Jim came down
the next morning, but his father was
in the living room looking at the paper.

"Come to breakfast," Mother called.

"In just a minute," answered Father.

In a little while Father came to breakfast.
"I know what a minute is now," said Jim.
"It is the morning paper."

"Look at my watch," said Jim's father.
"I will show you what a minute is."

Father told Jim to look at the long red hand that moved around the face of his watch. When it went all the way around once, he said, "There, that was a minute."

"Oh," said Jim. "Now I really know what a minute is. It is a long red hand that goes around the face of a watch."

Father jumped up and said, "I must go to work or I'll be late."

Mother just looked sad.

After school that day Jim asked Mother
to help him do his homework. When she said,
"In just a minute," Jim laughed.

"Will that be sixty seconds?" he asked.

"Sixty seconds!" Mother cried. "Oh, Jim,
you know what a minute is."

"Yes," said Jim. "My teacher said that
a real minute is always sixty seconds long.
The minute in JUST A MINUTE can be
long or short, but a real minute is always
just sixty seconds long."

WHEELS AND WINGS

THE BUS WITH THE FUNNY NAME

Debby jumped out of bed and ran quickly
to the window. It was not snowing!

"Oh, dear!" she thought as she ran back
to bed and pulled up the covers again.
"That old school bus will come today!"

Just then she heard her mother calling,
"Come, Debby, it is time to get up now.
The roads are all right, so I know that
the bus will be here soon. Please hurry."

"That's what I thought," said Debby.
She pushed the covers back and got slowly
out of bed. "Oh, dear!"

Debby looked so cross at breakfast that
her mother asked, "What is wrong?"

"I just don't like that old school bus,"
Debby answered quickly. "It is so old
that it rattles."

"Yes, the school should have a new bus,
but it should have many other things,
too," said Mother. "You will have to wait
a while for a new bus."

Soon the school bus rattled to a stop
at her house, and Debby got on. She sat
down back of Jake, the bus driver.

"We will have to have a new bus soon,"
Debby thought as the old bus rattled along.
"This one will rattle itself to pieces."

Soon she looked out of the window. Why,
it was snowing! The white snow was so wet
that it stuck to the window.

Then she tried to see out of the window
at the front, but something was wrong.
She could not see out because big pieces
of wet snow had stuck to the windshield.
How could Jake see?

Jake stopped the bus and turned around.
"Things don't look very good," he said.
"The windshield wipers are not working,
and I can't see the road."

"What can we do?" everyone asked.

"Well, there is one thing we could do,"
Jake said after he thought for a minute.
"Someone could sit up here on the floor
and move one windshield wiper by hand."

All the children started to say, "Let
me do it," but Jake looked right at Debby.
"The other children are all bigger than
you are, Debby, but this is something
that bigger children can't do," he said.
"Do you think you could do it?"

Debby jumped up. "Oh, yes," she said.
"Just show me what to do."

Jake told Debby to sit down in front
of the dashboard. Then he showed her how
to put her hands under the dashboard and
make the windshield wiper move.

Debby knew what to do, so Jake started
the bus. It went along very slowly.

The children were quiet. They looked
at Debby and hoped that she would keep
the windshield wiper moving.

Debby got so tired that her arms began
to hurt. Her head hurt, too, but she went
on moving the windshield wiper. Not once
did she stop to rest her arms.

Everyone was happy when the bus stopped
in front of the school. "Well, we made it,
Debby, thanks to you," said Jake.

When the people on the school board met
the next time, they talked about buying
a new school bus. One man said, "I think
we should buy a new bus now."

Another man said, "We have needed one
for a long time, but we didn't know how
much we needed it until that day when
the windshield wipers didn't work."

If people don't know what happened,
the name of the new bus may sound funny.
If people do know what happened that day,
the name DEBBY sounds wonderful!

THE SKY PONY

Little Bill and Big Bill were riding
with cowboys out on Big Bill's ranch.
Little Bill was riding his pony.

"Look, it is time for you to turn around
and start home," said Big Bill, who was
Little Bill's father. "The sun is away up
in the sky."

"Please let me ride on out with you,"
said Little Bill.

"Not today," said Big Bill. "We have
to ride far out to look for lost cattle,
and your pony is too slow for us."

Then Little Bill sadly started home.

Big Bill and the cowboys could not find
the lost cattle. "How many do you think
are gone?" asked Big Bill, after they came
back to the ranch house.

"I don't know," said the head cowboy.
"This ranch is so big that we can't keep
track of all the cattle."

"Why not let me help to keep track
of them?" asked Little Bill. "I can ride
my pony out to watch them."

"No, my boy," said Big Bill. "We need
another kind of pony to watch them."

The next morning Big Bill got up early
and left home to go to the city. He left
without telling anyone why he was going
or how long he would be gone.

Little Bill and the cowboys thought
each day that Big Bill would come back,
but he didn't. More than a week went by,
and still Big Bill was gone.

At last Little Bill got a short letter
from Big Bill. Here is what it said.

Dear Little Bill,

I'll be home Saturday with a new
kind of pony. It is bigger than your
pony.

Big Bill

Saturday morning Little Bill watched
for his father. Every minute he hoped that
Big Bill would come on his new pony.

By and by he heard a noise in the sky.
He looked up and saw something big flying
through the air. It had long arms that
turned round and round and went swish,
swish, swish through the air.

Soon it stopped going ahead and began
to come down slowly. It came right on
down to the ground.

There it sat on the ground with two men
inside. One of the men was Big Bill!

"Hello, Little Bill!" called Big Bill.
"How do you like my new pony?"

"Pony!" cried Little Bill. "That is
a helicopter! Is it really yours?"

"Yes, but I brought a man to drive it
until I learn how," answered Big Bill.
"Do you want to go for a ride?"

Little Bill got into the helicopter,
and away he went out over the ranch.

87

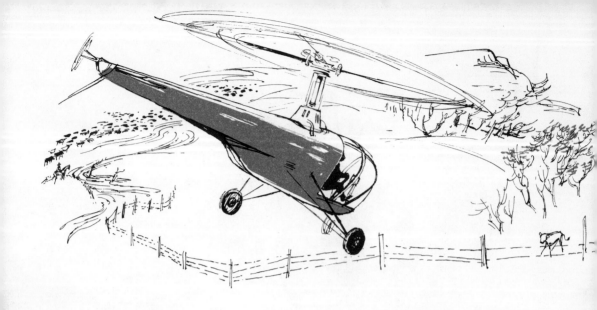

"Keep the helicopter near the ground
so we can see things," said Big Bill.

Little Bill looked down at the cattle
and fences and fields on the big ranch.
Soon he called, "Oh, look! Down there
near a fence is a little calf."

"We will pick it up and take it back
to its mother," said Big Bill.

In a minute or two the little calf was
in the helicopter going back to its mother,
far across the field.

"Now I know why you said that you had
a new kind of pony," said Little Bill.
"The helicopter is a sky pony!"

A TERRIBLE TAXI RIDE

If you live in a little town like ours,
you know that everyone always knows all
about everyone else. Nothing can happen
without everyone knowing about it.

So, when something happened to Maxie,
everyone else found out about it.

Maxie had a taxi. It was a good taxi,
as taxis go, but sometimes his didn't.
It was still the very best taxi in town,
because there was no other.

On one dark, cold, wet, terrible day,
Mrs. T. Worthington Smith called Maxie
on the telephone. "I would like a taxi,"
she said in her most ladylike voice.

Mrs. T. Worthington Smith always tried
to sound like a great lady. She had lived
in a city—a great big city!

Oh, dear, but Maxie was cross. It was
such a terrible day to be out. Besides,
he didn't want to take that Mrs. Smith
anywhere. She was a back seat driver.

Maxie didn't want to go, but he did.
Mrs. T. Worthington Smith was waiting
for him with a big covered basket.

"Now what?" Maxie thought to himself
as he drove up, for he never knew just what
that woman would do.

She smiled her most ladylike smile and
said, "Take this basket to the last house
on First Street."

Maxie could have jumped up and down
on the seat! He had to take the basket,
but NOT Mrs. T. Worthington Smith!

He never had been so happy! Off he drove
without giving a thought to the kind of day.
He didn't care how dark and wet and cold
and terrible it was.

All at once something tickled his neck.
He laughed at first and said, "Stop that."
Then he remembered that he was alone.

Something tickled his neck again!

Something jumped on his back!

HE WAS NOT ALONE!

Maxie turned around quickly to find
out who or what was in his taxi. "Cats!"
he shouted. "My taxi is full of cats!"

There were cats on the back seat, cats
on the front seat, cats all over the taxi.
That covered basket had been full of cats!
Maxie was so busy with cats that he just
could not keep his hands on the wheel.

People on the street began to shout,
"Look at that taxi! The driver can't keep
his hands on the wheel."

93

Crash! Bang! Maxie's taxi went right up
on the sidewalk and crashed into a store.

The six cats were the first to climb out.
They ran all over the store. People tried
to catch them, but they could not.

A man came to take a picture of Maxie
and his taxi and the cats. "I must have
the cats in the picture," he said.

He put some pieces of fish in the taxi,
and the cats came hurrying back. They got
the fish, and the man got the picture!

That is what happened to Maxie.
At the time he didn't think that
the terrible taxi ride was funny,
but now he laughs about it.

He laughs because he thinks that
two nice things happened to him
after that terrible taxi ride.

When he tried to take the cats
to the last house on First Street,
he found that no one lived there.

When he tried to take them back
to Mrs. T. Worthington Smith,
he found that she had moved back
to the city that very day.

He never has to take that woman
anywhere in his taxi, and he thinks
that is nice. The six cats moved in
with him, and he thinks that is
very nice, too.

MR. PUNNYMOON'S TRAIN

This story tells about Mr. Punnymoon,
who drove a big engine on a train. He was
a good engineer, and he took very good care
of his great big engine.

Mr. Punnymoon liked to start the engine
and hear it go CHOO-CHOO-CHOO.

He liked to make the wheels go around
so fast that they went clickety-clack,
clickety-clack over the tracks.

Most of all, he liked to hear the sound
of the engine whistle. He liked to make the
whistle go WHOOOO-WHO-WHOOOO.

At last Mr. Punnymoon became too old
to work on the railroad. He had to stop
being an engineer.

The last day he worked for the railroad
was a big day for him. Many people came
to surprise him when he brought his engine
down the tracks for the last time.

A big man from the railroad told what
a good engineer Mr. Punnymoon had been.
The railroad was proud of him.

Mr. Punnymoon was very proud, too.

The next day Mr. Punnymoon's wife knew
that he was thinking about his big engine.
He didn't know what to do with himself.

"Why don't you go out to your workshop
and make something?" asked his wife.

"The very thing!" said Mr. Punnymoon,
and he went to his workshop at once.

"I only know about engines," he thought.
"I guess I'll have to make an engine."

So he started. He worked day after day
and week after week until at last he had
an engine. It was just like a real engine,
only it was little.

One day some neighbor children heard
a whistle in Mr. Punnymoon's back yard.
They ran to see what was happening.

"Oh! A little engine!" they shouted.
"Will it run?"

"Yes, it will run," said Mr. Punnymoon.
"Let me show you."

He made the little engine go a short way
in his yard. "See, it runs," he said.

"Then make some little cars and take us
for a ride!" shouted the children.

"The very thing!" said Mr. Punnymoon.
"Why didn't I think of that?"

Mr. Punnymoon made five small cars
for the neighbor children. Each car had
seats where the children could sit.

Now Mr. Punnymoon had a real train
with an engine and five cars. He looked
around for a good place to run the train
and found that his yard was too small.
"What shall I do?" he cried.

"Why not take the train to the park?"
asked a neighbor boy.

"The very thing," said Mr. Punnymoon.
"Then we would have room for tracks."

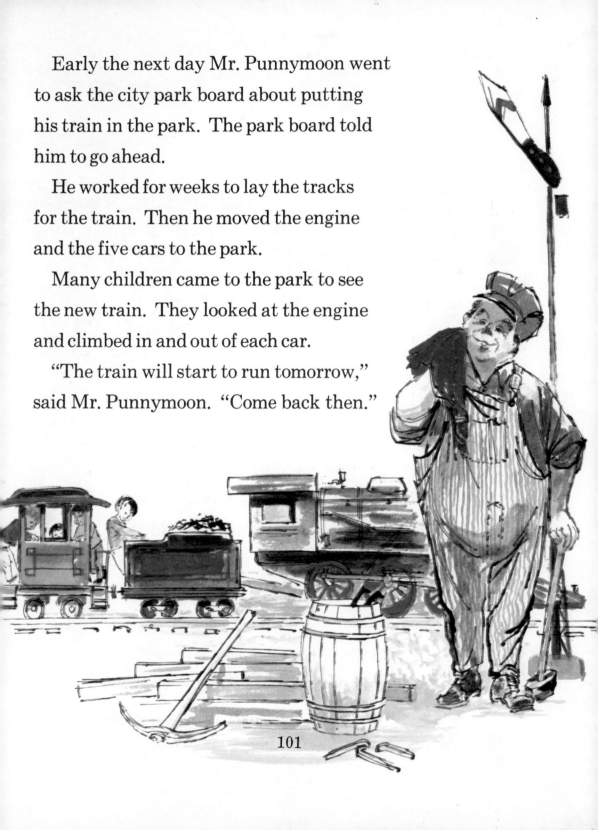

Early the next day Mr. Punnymoon went
to ask the city park board about putting
his train in the park. The park board told
him to go ahead.

He worked for weeks to lay the tracks
for the train. Then he moved the engine
and the five cars to the park.

Many children came to the park to see
the new train. They looked at the engine
and climbed in and out of each car.

"The train will start to run tomorrow,"
said Mr. Punnymoon. "Come back then."

When the children came the next day,
Mr. Punnymoon looked like a conductor.
He had a new cap with letters that said
CONDUCTOR across the front.

Mr. Punnymoon's wife was there, too.
She gave each of the children a ticket
for a ride on the train.

Soon Mr. Punnymoon went to the train
and shouted in his best conductor's voice,
"All aboard! All aboard!"

The children quickly found their seats
on the cars. Mr. Punnymoon walked along
beside them and took the tickets.
When he came to the engine, he put on
his engineer's cap. Then he took a seat
on the engine and started the train.

Today he is happy and does not miss
driving his big engine on the railroad.
He does not miss it because he is busy
driving his little engine in the park.

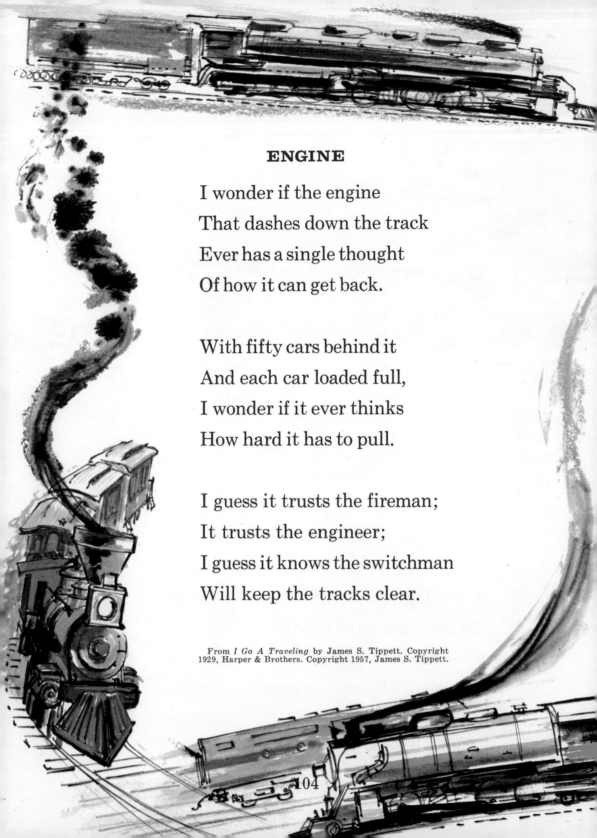

ENGINE

I wonder if the engine
That dashes down the track
Ever has a single thought
Of how it can get back.

With fifty cars behind it
And each car loaded full,
I wonder if it ever thinks
How hard it has to pull.

I guess it trusts the fireman;
It trusts the engineer;
I guess it knows the switchman
Will keep the tracks clear.

From *I Go A Traveling* by James S. Tippett. Copyright 1929, Harper & Brothers. Copyright 1957, James S. Tippett.

MOSTLY NONSENSE

THE MAGIC BUBBLE

One day a boy named Jack was blowing
bubbles in his back yard and thinking
it would be fun to ride in a bubble.

"If only I could blow magic bubbles,
I might ride in one," he thought.

Then, all at once, he began to blow
magic bubbles. Each bubble was bigger
than the one before, and at last he had
one so big that he could step into it.

Into the bubble he went, and, SWISH,
up in the air he went.

What a wonderful ride Jack had! There
he sat in the big magic bubble and floated
away up into the sky.

At first he was very happy. "This is
the best ride I ever have had," he said.

The bubble floated on and on. At last
he began to think, "Where am I going?
How will I ever get back?"

Now he was just a little afraid. Here
he was high up in the air without a way
to get down. The bubble would only take
him higher and higher.

Soon he was up so high that everything was cold. The big bubble was covered all over with ice.

When Jack saw the ice, he was really afraid. How could he ever get home?

Then he looked out again and was surprised to see something that would help him. It was a long icicle running all the way down to the ground.

He jumped on the icicle and down he went, PLOP, into his back yard.

Now you may think that he didn't go up in a bubble and come down on an icicle, but he did. He really did!

GOING TO ST. IVES

As I was going to St. Ives,

I met a man with seven wives.

Each wife had seven sacks;

Each sack had seven cats;

Each cat had seven kits.

Kits, cats, sacks, and wives,

How many were going to St. Ives?

IF ALL THE SEAS

If all the seas were one sea,
What a great sea that would be!
If all the trees were one tree,
What a great tree that would be!
If all the axes were one ax,
What a great ax that would be!
If all the men were one man,
What a great man he would be!
And if the great man took the great ax,
And cut down the great tree,
And let it fall into the great sea,
What a great splash-splash that would be!

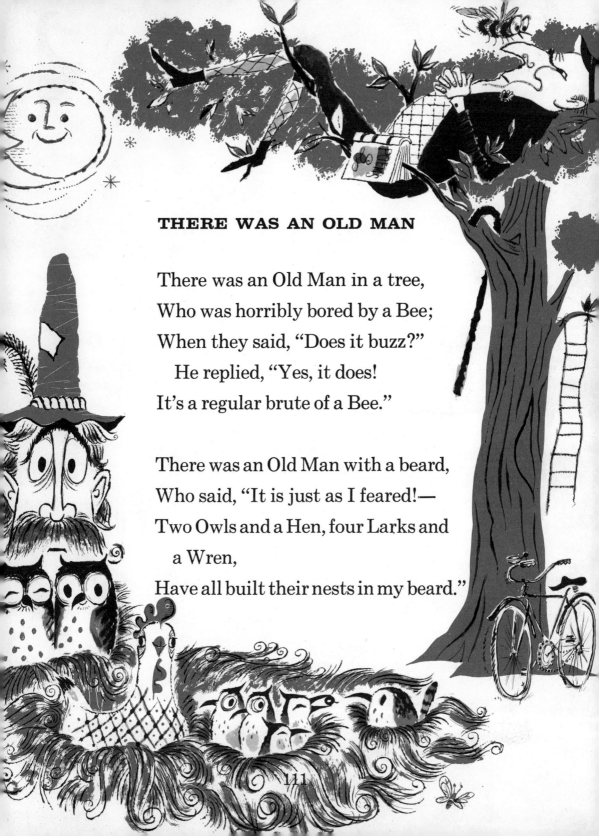

THERE WAS AN OLD MAN

There was an Old Man in a tree,
Who was horribly bored by a Bee;
When they said, "Does it buzz?"
   He replied, "Yes, it does!
It's a regular brute of a Bee."

There was an Old Man with a beard,
Who said, "It is just as I feared!—
Two Owls and a Hen, four Larks and
   a Wren,
Have all built their nests in my beard."

WHAT YOU DO

When you go to a zoo, you look.
When you go to the kitchen, you cook.

When you go on a plane, you fly.
When you go to a sale, you buy.

When you go on a bus, you ride.
When you go to a dance, you glide.

When you go to a school, you learn.
When you work for money, you earn.

When you go to a store, you shop.
When you run out of money, you stop!

112

THE MAN AND HIS GOOSE

"I am tired of working," said an old man one day. "If I had all the money I wanted, I would make a nice little house and spend my time fishing."

Just then a good little witch came along with a bag full of money. "You may have all this money, but you will only make a goose of yourself with it," she said.

"Not I," said the old man quickly.

"Wait and see," said the little witch, and she went away.

The old man made a nice little house.

The old man moved into his nice house
and began to build a pond in his back yard.
"I'll leave a place out in the pond where
I can sit and fish," he said.

He was almost through building the pond
when the witch came back. She took a look
at his house and pond and said, "I told you
that you would make a goose of yourself.
You are making a good start."

"I'm just building a pond and leaving
a place in it where I can sit and fish,"
said the old man.

The witch looked again. "Wait and see,"
she said. Then she left.

Next the old man made two flower beds.
He made them near the pond, and he planted
bright yellow flowers in them.

Every day he went to the pond and fished.
Then he went to one flower bed or the other
and picked the bright yellow flowers that
he had planted.

"I'm proud of my house and my pond and
my flower beds," he said to himself one day
while he was fishing. "I'm proud to think
that I have not made a big goose of myself
with that bag full of money."

"But you have," said a voice beside him,
and there was the witch. "Walk up this hill
with me, and I'll show you."

They went up the hill and looked down. "Now do you believe me?" asked the witch.

The old man was surprised. "Well, well!" he said at last. "I would not have believed it if I had not seen it."

Then he laughed and said, "I'm glad that my house, my pond, and my flower beds look like a goose. I'm glad that I made a goose of myself that way. Thanks for your help, witch. Thanks a lot."

IF ALL THE WORLD

If all the world were apple pie
And all the sea were ink,
And all the trees were bread and cheese,
What should we have to drink?

THE CANDLE

Little Nancy Etticoat,
In her white petticoat
And a red nose,
The longer she stands,
The shorter she grows.

THE MERRY CHASE

Through the garden,
Where I sat,
And into the house,
Across the mat,
A cow chased a zebra,
Chasing a cat,
Chasing a leopard,
Chasing a rat,
Chasing a lion,

Chasing a bat,
Chasing a frog
That was ugly and fat,
Chasing a man
Who was chasing his hat—
And what
An exciting
Chase
Was that!

FAIRY SHOES

The little shoes that fairies wear
    Are very small indeed;
No larger than a violet bud,
    As tiny as a seed.

The little shoes that fairies wear
    Are very trim and neat;
They leave no tracks behind for those
    Who search along the street.

The little shoes of fairies are
    So light and soft and small
That though a million passed you by,
    You would not hear them at all.

HAPPY HOLIDAYS

MIKE'S HALLOWEEN PUMPKIN

Mike was little, and the pumpkin was big and round. He was taking the pumpkin to school for Halloween.

Mike stopped at the corner and waited for the policeman to tell him when to go across the street.

He was so little that he could not see over the pumpkin very well. All at once he fell on the pumpkin.

"Can you make my pumpkin big and round again?" Mike asked the policeman.

"No," said the policeman. "I'm afraid you will have to find a new one."

Mike picked up the pieces of pumpkin and went on. When he came to a firehouse, he showed the pieces to a fireman.

"I fell on my pumpkin," he said sadly. "Can you make it big and round again?"

"I'm sorry, but you must try to find a new one," said the fireman.

Mike went on. He saw Mr. Shoemaker, the man who worked on shoes.

"Mr. Shoemaker, can you make my pumpkin big and round again?" he asked.

"I'm sorry, but you must try to find a new one," said Mr. Shoemaker.

Mike asked Mr. Fix-it, who was fixing
a car. He asked Mr. Baker, who was baking
a birthday cake. He asked Mr. Cleaner,
who was cleaning a dress.

He asked Mr. Builder and Mr. Painter,
who were building and painting a house.
At last he asked Mr. Neighbor, who was
always kind and good.

Mike asked them all the same thing,
but they all gave him the same answer.
They could not make his pumpkin big and
round again. He needed a new one.

"Well, I'll take the pieces to school," said Mike. "Maybe my teacher can make my pumpkin big and round again."

"What are those?" asked the children when they saw the pieces.

"What are those?" asked the teacher.

"Pieces of pumpkin," said Mike. "I fell and broke my big pumpkin. Can you make it big and round again?"

"I can try," said the teacher.

While the other children looked at books or painted pictures, the teacher worked on the pumpkin with Mike.

Before long the children heard someone at the door. Then in walked the policeman with a big fat pumpkin.

"I want to see Mike Brown," he said. "He needs a pumpkin, so I have brought one for him."

When the policeman handed the pumpkin to Mike, he said, "Is it big enough?"

"Oh, yes!" said Mike. "Thank you."

Minutes later Mike looked out and saw the fireman drive up with a fat pumpkin on the seat beside him.

"What?" cried Mike. "Two pumpkins! One would have been enough!"

Soon another car stopped at the school,
and Mr. Shoemaker got out with a pumpkin.

"Three pumpkins!" cried Mike.

Next came Mr. Fix-it with a fat pumpkin.
Then there were four pumpkins. Just back
of him came Mr. Baker and Mr. Cleaner
with pumpkins. Then there were six.

Last came a farmer with some pumpkins
on a truck. Three people had asked him
to bring them—Mr. Builder, Mr. Painter,
and Mr. Neighbor.

"Take my fat new pumpkins and have fun with them," Mike told the children.

They made funny pumpkin faces and put them in the windows. Soon Mike brought his old pumpkin pieced together. "Here is another one," he said.

"Good!" shouted the children. "We like your old pumpkin face. It is the very best one of all." And it was, too!

GUESS WHAT DAY

There's a turkey in the oven,
   Pumpkin pies to eat;
Stuffing, chestnuts, cranberries;
   It is a special treat.

With families all together,
   Their happy faces bright;
Can you guess what day this is?
   Thanksgiving Day, that's right!

SANTA CLAUS ON THE MOON

It was only two days before Christmas, and Santa Claus was busy. All at once Whoosh and Whish, two of his helpers, saw strange things happening in the sky.

The moon was giving off bright moonlight as never before, and far out in the sky Santa's reindeer were running away.

"Jiminy Christmas!" cried Santa Claus. "This is terrible! My reindeer are running away, and I need them for Christmas. What shall I do?"

Mrs. Claus, who was baking cookies, came
to see what was happening.

Santa and his helpers ran to the barn
to find out how many reindeer were gone,
but not a reindeer was there.

Then Santa looked around outside the
barn and found a letter tacked on the door.

The letter said:

> If you want your reindeer,
> come to the moon.
>
> The one and only
> Man in the Moon

"Oh, dear!" cried Mrs. Claus. "Now how will the children get their Christmas toys? How will they get my cookies?"

"They won't, if I stand here and leave my reindeer on the moon," answered Santa. "I must go to the moon after them at once, but how can I get there?"

"I know," said Whish. "Whoosh can take you there in his spaceship."

"Yes, yes, the spaceship!" cried Santa. "You will take me, won't you, Whoosh?"

"Well, I never have gone to the moon, but I can try," said Whoosh.

"Let us go, then," shouted Santa.

Whoosh and Santa ran to the spaceship behind the workshop. There it was standing with its nose high in the air.

"Wait!" called Mrs. Claus. "I'll fill a bag with cookies for you to take along. It won't take a minute."

She filled a bag fast and came flying back. Then Whoosh climbed into the ship, with Santa right behind him.

Santa looked out a window and waved to Mrs. Claus, standing by the ship.

She waved back at him. Then, SWISH, the spaceship left the ground so fast that she could hardly see it!

The spaceship went higher and higher, and something strange happened to Santa. He began to float around in the ship as if he were a balloon.

"What is happening?" cried Santa, trying to hold onto his seat.

Whoosh laughed. "Don't be afraid, Santa," he said. "We are just out in space."

"Yes, I know, but why am I floating as if I were a balloon?" asked Santa.

"Because away out here in space there is little to hold us down," said Whoosh. "You will have to tie yourself down."

So Santa tied himself to his seat.

Soon Whoosh called to Santa, "Hold on! We are about ready to land."

He landed the spaceship on the moon, and Santa shouted, "Well, we made it! You stay here to look after the spaceship, and I'll try to find my reindeer."

Santa climbed out and started to walk, but he found it hard to stand up. He had a hard time keeping his feet on the ground. Every step turned into a jump.

All at once a strange man came jumping up. He had a big round face, so Santa knew he was the Man in the Moon. He seemed surprised to see Santa.

"Hello," said Santa. "You seem surprised to see me. Didn't you think I would come after my reindeer?"

"No, I didn't," said the Man in the Moon. "I thought you didn't need them."

"How could you think anything so foolish as that?" asked Santa.

"Well, it does not seem foolish to me," said the Man in the Moon. "You have both an airplane and a helicopter. I thought you would use one of them."

Santa threw his head back and laughed. "I have both an airplane and a helicopter that I can use for many things," he said. "However, I would not THINK of using them on the night before Christmas!"

Now the Man in the Moon threw his head back and laughed. "Your reindeer will be glad to know that," he said. "They came to the moon with me because they thought you didn't need them any more."

"Where are they?" asked Santa.

"Back in the mountains," said the Man in the Moon. "I'll take you to them."

137

When the reindeer saw Santa, they ran
down the mountainside to him. They were
glad he still needed them.

"You may ride back in the spaceship,"
Santa told them. "Then you will be rested
for the night before Christmas!"

The reindeer climbed into the spaceship,
and the Man in the Moon shouted,
"Merry Christmas!"

Then, as the spaceship went out of sight,
he heard Santa calling, "Merry Christmas
to all, and to all a good night!"

BUNDLES

A bundle is a funny thing,
It always sets me wondering;
For whether it is thin or wide
You never know just what's inside.

Especially on Christmas week,
Temptation is so great to peek!
Now wouldn't it be much more fun
If shoppers carried things undone?

VALENTINES FOR L-L

Linda-Lou and Laura-Lee lived next door to one another. They were as much alike as two bluebirds in the same tree. Sometimes they even thought alike.

Every morning they walked to school together. After school and on Saturdays, they played together. Most other times, they just WERE together.

The two girls were together so much that sometimes even their mothers hardly knew which girl lived in which house!

So no one knows why the girls quarreled,
but quarrel they did. One snowy winter day
Linda-Lou ran into her house crying.

At the same time on the same winter day,
Laura-Lee ran into her house crying.
Both girls were crying so hard they forgot
to take off their mittens.

Both mothers asked, "What is wrong?"
Both girls cried into their mittens harder
than ever and didn't say anything.

Linda-Lou and Laura-Lee didn't talk,
but their mothers knew what had happened.
Tomorrow was Valentine Day, too!

Linda-Lou's mother began to take things out of a box on the table. "Did you forget about making valentines?" she asked.

Linda-Lou slowly moved one wet mitten away from one eye and looked at the box. Then she moved the other wet mitten away from the other eye and smiled.

"I almost forgot," she said as she went over to the table and began to work.

"Don't you want Laura-Lee to come and help you?" asked her mother.

"No, thank you," Linda-Lou said quickly. "It would be too hard to be nice. We ended our friendship today, and I don't even want to talk with Laura-Lee now."

Linda-Lou worked alone all afternoon.
"It is better this way," she told herself,
but she didn't really believe it.

She made a pretty valentine for everyone
she knew—everyone, that is, but Laura-Lee.
She signed each one, "From Linda-Lou."

By the end of the afternoon, she was all
through. She looked at the valentines and
thought of Laura-Lee. She knew which one
Laura-Lee would have liked best.

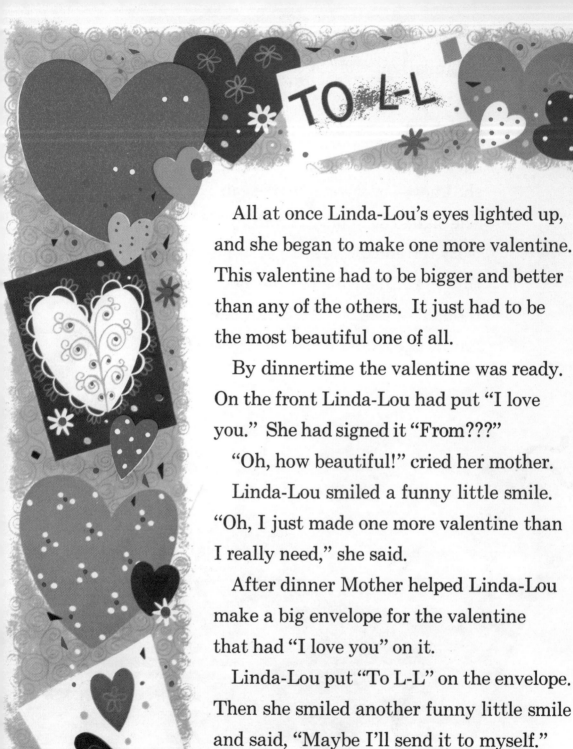

All at once Linda-Lou's eyes lighted up, and she began to make one more valentine. This valentine had to be bigger and better than any of the others. It just had to be the most beautiful one of all.

By dinnertime the valentine was ready. On the front Linda-Lou had put "I love you." She had signed it "From???"

"Oh, how beautiful!" cried her mother.

Linda-Lou smiled a funny little smile. "Oh, I just made one more valentine than I really need," she said.

After dinner Mother helped Linda-Lou make a big envelope for the valentine that had "I love you" on it.

Linda-Lou put "To L-L" on the envelope. Then she smiled another funny little smile and said, "Maybe I'll send it to myself."

144

Early the next morning Linda-Lou ran
to Laura-Lee's house with the big envelope
in her hands. Quiet as a cat she went up
the front steps and put the big envelope
beside the letter box.

She looked around. No one had seen her.
Then she rang the doorbell and ran home
into the warm kitchen.

Linda-Lou's mother was in the kitchen
getting breakfast. "Someone just rang
our doorbell," she said as Linda-Lou came
through the back door.

145

Linda-Lou ran to open the front door.
She didn't see anyone, but she did see
a big white envelope with "To L-L" on it.
Inside was the most beautiful valentine
that Linda-Lou ever had seen.

"Why, it is almost like the one I made,"
she said. It had "I love you" on the front,
and "From ???" on the back.

Linda-Lou ran to the kitchen and said,
"If I'm going to meet Laura-Lee, I must
not be LATE."

In the kitchen next door, Laura-Lee was
saying, "If I'm going to meet Linda-Lou,
I must not make her WAIT."

146

EASTER BUNNY'S BIG NIGHT

Mrs. Bunny was singing as she put eggs
into Easter Bunny's bright red basket
on the night before Easter. "Hop, hop,
hop, until it is time to stop."

"I have used that song for years and
years, but I won't use it this year,"
Easter Bunny told her. "I can't use it
because I'm not going to hop this year.
I'm going to use a car."

"A car!" cried Mrs. Bunny in surprise. "Where under the sun did you get a car?"

"The old goat down the road fixed one up for me," said Easter Bunny. "I'm going to get it now."

"Did you buy it?" asked Mrs. Bunny.

"Oh, no. I'm going to use it tonight," said Easter Bunny. "If I like it, then I'll buy it."

Easter Bunny hopped away and soon rode back in a funny-looking, rattly-bang car. He stopped it with a bang and a bump.

Mrs. Bunny heard the car and came out with the basket of Easter eggs.

"Well, what do you think of the car?"
Easter Bunny asked proudly.

"I'm not sure," answered Mrs. Bunny.
"I can't help wishing that you would hop
this year, as you always have."

Easter Bunny didn't even listen. He was
ready to start out. He pushed one thing,
and he pulled another thing. He stepped
on something else. Then the car moved,
but not the way he wanted it to. It went
back with a jump and a bump!

"Dear me! Are you sure that you know
how to drive?" cried Mrs. Bunny.

Easter Bunny didn't answer. He tried
again, and this time the car went ahead.
"Good-by," he called as he rode off.

Easter Bunny drove very fast. He was pleased to have the rattly-bang old car. Now he would not have to hop his way across fields. He could go on the road.

When it got a little darker, he turned on the headlights. "I don't know for sure where I am," he said to himself. "It is funny, but I can't see as well as when I hop. These lights are too bright."

Just then he saw a big bump in the road ahead. "Better go over it," he thought. "I'll go up one side and down the other!" So he drove faster than ever.

It really was too bad that he didn't take time to find out what the bump was. It was a cow, asleep. When the car started to go over her, she jumped up and ran away.

The car turned over, and the eggs fell out of the basket. They rolled down the hill into a field beside the road.

Easter Bunny landed in the field, too, in a muddy spot. He sat there in the dark, holding his head and saying, "Where am I? Where are my eggs?"

He looked around and what he saw made him afraid. The field was full of holes! "If these holes belong to foxes, I landed in a bad spot," he thought.

Something began to come up, very slowly, out of one of the holes. Easter Bunny sat there, waiting. He was too afraid to move. Then he saw that two ears were coming out of the hole—two long ears. Rabbits lived in these holes, not foxes!

"What happened?" asked a bunny voice. "An egg came rolling into my hole."

"Some eggs rolled into our holes, too," cried other bunny voices.

"Those are my eggs," said Easter Bunny. "They fell out of a basket I was carrying in my car. Don't you know who I am?"

The rabbits looked again. "Now we do," they said. "We will bring the eggs back. You must carry them to the children."

Rabbits came from all over, bringing eggs
back to Easter Bunny. They helped him put
the eggs in the basket again. They turned
his car right side up.

"What are you doing with this old car?"
they asked. "Why don't you use your legs
and hop? Leave the car here and pick it up
on your way home."

"I believe I will," said Easter Bunny.
He started off with the basket, taking
long hops on his own strong legs.

After he had left the last Easter egg
at the last place, he hopped back to get
the car. He drove fast on the way home,
but he watched for bumps.

It was almost daylight when he got home, but his wife was waiting for him. "Are you all right?" she called. "How did you get along with your driving?"

He told her about the bump that jumped up and ran away.

"Will you buy the car?" she asked.

"No, my feet are long and strong,
And it is fun to hop along.
I'll take care of Easter eggs,
Hopping on my own strong legs!"

"What a lovely song!" cried Mrs. Bunny. "I like it much better than 'Hop, hop, hop, until it is time to stop!'"

"Well, it is time to stop now, my dear, until next year," said Easter Bunny.

FUN AND FANCY

FOOLISH JACK

Jack and his old mother lived together
in the country. They had almost no money.
The old mother worked hard, but Jack sat
in the sun and did nothing.

One day his mother said to him, "Jack,
if you will not work, you cannot eat."

Then Jack went out into the country
and found work for one day with a farmer.
The farmer gave him a penny for his work,
but Jack lost the penny on his way home.

"You foolish boy!" said his old mother.
"You should have put it in your pocket."

"I'll do so another time," said Jack.

The next day Jack went out again and
worked for a farmer who gave him a jar
of milk for his day's work.

Jack took the jar, which did not have
any cover, and put it into the pocket
of his coat. By the time he got home,
his pocket was wet and the milk was gone.

"You foolish boy!" said his old mother.
"You cannot carry milk in the pocket
of your coat. You should have put the jar
on your head."

"I'll do so another time," said Jack.

The following day Jack went out again
to work for another farmer, who gave him
some butter for his day's work.

Jack took the butter and started home
with it on his head. The day was very hot.
Before he got home, the butter had run
into his eyes and ears and down his neck.

"You foolish boy!" said his old mother.
"You should have brought the butter home
in your hands."

"I'll do so another time," said Jack.

The day following that, Jack went out again and worked for a baker, who gave him nothing but a big cat for his work.

Jack took the cat in his hands and tried to carry it home, but the big cat jumped around so much he had to let it go.

When he got home his old mother said, "You foolish boy! You should have tied the big cat with a string and pulled it along the road after you."

"I'll do so another time," said Jack.

The next day Jack worked for a butcher. The butcher gave him a good piece of meat for his day's work.

Jack took the piece of meat and tied it with a string and pulled it along the road after him. When he got home, the meat was not any good to eat.

"You foolish boy!" said his old mother. "You should have brought the piece of meat home on your shoulder."

"I'll do so another time," said Jack.

The next day Jack went again and worked
for a farmer, who gave him a donkey.

Jack tied the donkey's legs and put it
on his shoulder. He had all he could do
to carry the donkey home.

Now it happened that in the town there
lived a rich man who had an only daughter.
She never had laughed, so her father said
he would give a big bag of gold to anyone
who could make her laugh.

Jack had to go by the rich man's house
to get to his own home. When he came along
with a donkey on his shoulder, he looked
so funny that the daughter laughed.

Her father and mother were very happy.
They called Jack in at once and gave him
a big bag of gold.

How he got home with both the donkey
and the gold, no one ever has heard.

THE LION AND THE MOUSE

Once when a big yellow lion was asleep
in the forest, a little gray mouse began
to run up and down his back. He sat up
and caught the mouse in his great paw.

He opened his great mouth, for he wanted
to eat the little mouse. The mouse cried,
"Oh, do not eat me, Mr. Lion. Some day
I may do you a good turn."

At this, the lion laughed and laughed,
but he let the little gray mouse go.

The next day some men came to the forest
and caught the lion in a trap. They wanted
to take the lion back to the city alive,
so they took him out of the trap and tied
him to a tree. Then they went away to look
for a wagon.

The little gray mouse came along and saw
the lion tied to a tree. At once she began
to gnaw the ropes with which he was tied.
She gnawed one rope in two. Then she gnawed
another rope and another and another. Soon
she had gnawed away all the ropes.

"I told you I might do you a good turn
some day," she said. "Little friends may
sometimes be great friends."

THE MAN WHO KEPT HOUSE

Once upon a time there was a man who was so cross that he thought his wife never did anything right around the house. One night in haymaking time, he came home even more cross than he had been before.

"Dear husband, please don't be so cross," said his wife. "How would it be if we do each other's work tomorrow? I'll go out and work in the hayfield if you will stay here and keep house."

The man thought that would do very well, so early the next morning his wife went out to work in the hayfield. The husband stayed at home and kept house.

First of all, the man started to churn
some butter. After churning for a while,
he thought he would like to have a pickle.
So he went to the cellar to get one.

He took the cover off the big jar and got
out a pickle. Just then he heard a noise
overhead. It sounded as if the pig had come
into the kitchen.

Off he ran up the cellar steps as fast as
he could run. He wanted to keep the pig
from overturning the churn.

When he got to the kitchen he found out
that he was too late. The pig had knocked
the churn over, and the cream was running
all over the floor.

The man was so cross with the pig that
he forgot everything else and ran after it.
He caught up with it, too, just as it ran
out the door. He gave it such a hard blow
that he knocked the pig over.

Right then he remembered that he had not
put the cover back on the pickle jar. So
he went to the cellar. When he got there,
he found a mouse in the pickle jar.

167

The man knew there would be no butter
for dinner if he didn't churn some. So
he found enough cream to fill the churn
again and went on with his work.

While he was churning, he remembered
that the cow was still in the barn. She had not
had anything to eat or drink all morning.

"Well," he thought. "I don't have time
to take her out to the field. I'll just put her
up on top of the house."

The house, you must know, was covered
with ground. Good green grass was growing
on the housetop.

168

The house stood on the side of a hill,
and the man thought he could lay boards
from the hill across to the housetop. Then
the cow could walk across on the boards and
eat the grass growing on the housetop.

Still, he could not very well go away
from the kitchen now. The baby was playing
on the floor, and he did not like to leave
her near the churn.

He stood there, leaning on the table, and
thought for a minute. "The baby might
knock the churn over," he said to himself.

In the end, he put the churn on his back and took it out with him. Then he thought he should water the cow before he put her up on the housetop to eat grass.

He took a bucket and went to the well to get some water. When he leaned over to pull the bucket up, all the cream ran out of the churn and into the well.

He put the cow on the housetop and went back to the kitchen. Now it was almost time for dinner, but he had not done much work. He thought it would be best to go ahead and make some porridge, so he filled a big pan with water and put it on the fire.

When he had done that, he remembered
the cow was on the housetop. She might fall
off and hurt herself. So up he went to tie
her fast. One end of the long rope he tied
around the cow's neck. The other end he put
down the chimney.

Then he ran back to the kitchen and tied
this end to his own leg. "Now the cow can't
fall off and hurt herself," he thought.

While he was making porridge, the cow fell
off the housetop, after all. The rope pulled
the man up the chimney, and there he stuck
fast. The cow was left hanging in the air,
about four feet from the ground.

171

Now the wife had been waiting a long time
for her husband to call her home to dinner.
At last she thought she had waited long
enough, and she went to the house.

When she saw the cow hanging in the air,
she ran up and cut the long rope in two. As
soon as she cut the rope, the cow came down
to the ground.

And when the wife went into the kitchen,
she found her husband standing on his head
in the porridge pan.

THE LITTLE ELF

I met a little elf man once,
  Down where the lilies blow;
I asked him why he was so small,
  And why he did not grow.

He slightly frowned, and with his eye
  He looked me through and through;
"I'm quite as big for me," said he,
  "As you are big for you."

"The Little Elf" by John Kendrick Bangs from *St. Nicholas Book of Verse.* Copyright 1923, Century Company. Reprinted by permission of the publisher, Appleton-Century-Crofts, Inc.

THE THREE GOATS

Once upon a time there were three goats
who lived in a big field. The goats were
very hungry because they had no more grass
to eat in the field.

There was green grass in the big forest,
but the hungry goats had to cross a bridge
to get there.

Now under the bridge lived an old Troll
with big ears and an ugly long nose.
The Troll did not like the goats.

One day Little Goat said, "I am going
across the bridge to the forest. I want
to eat green grass in the forest."

Big Goat said, "Oh, please do not go,
Little Goat. The ugly old Troll will come
out and eat you."

"I am not afraid of the ugly old Troll,"
said Little Goat. "He will not eat me
because I am too little."

So Little Goat went on.

The old Troll heard Little Goat's feet
on the bridge, Trip-trap! Trip-trap!
Trip-trap! "Who runs on my bridge?"
he cried in a loud voice.

"Just Little Goat," answered the goat
in a very small voice. "I am on my way
to the forest to eat grass."

"You cannot cross my bridge for grass,"
said the Troll. "I will eat you."

"Oh, do not eat me," said Little Goat.
"I am too little. Soon Big Goat will come.
He is much bigger to eat."

"Go on, then," said the old Troll.

After a while Big Goat came running fast
across the bridge. The old Troll heard
Big Goat's feet on the bridge, Trip-trap!
Trip-trap! Trip-trap!

"Who runs on my bridge?" he called out
in his loud voice.

"It is just Big Goat," answered the goat
in a strong voice. "I am going to the forest
to eat grass."

"You cannot cross my bridge for grass,"
said the Troll. "I will eat you."

"Do not eat me," said Big Goat. "I am
not big. Soon Great Big Goat will come.
He is very big."

"Go on, then," said the old Troll.

Then Great Big Goat came to the bridge.
He was so big that he made the bridge move
this way and that. The old Troll heard
Great Big Goat's big feet on the bridge,
Trip-trap! Trip-trap! Trip-trap!

"Who runs on my bridge?" he called out
in a very loud voice.

"Great Big Goat," said Great Big Goat
in his great loud voice. "I am on my way
to the forest to eat grass."

"You cannot cross my bridge for grass,"
said the Troll. "I will eat you."

"Come on, then," said Great Big Goat.
"Come on. Eat me if you can."

Then Great Big Goat put down his horns.
When the old Troll climbed on the bridge,
Great Big Goat ran into him with his horns.

He ran so fast that he knocked the Troll
right off the bridge. Then he walked on
across the bridge to the forest.

After that all three goats ate the grass
in the forest.

Little Goat ate some grass. Big Goat ate
more grass. But Great Big Goat, who knocked
the Troll off the bridge, ate most of all.

And if the grass is not all gone by now,
they are still eating there.

AT THE SEASIDE

When I was down beside the sea,
A wooden spade they gave to me
  To dig the sandy shore.

My holes were empty like a cup;
In every hole the sea came up,
  Till it could come no more.

CINDERELLA

Long ago there was a rich man who had
three daughters. The youngest daughter was
beautiful and as good as she was beautiful.
The two older girls, who were bad and ugly,
did not like their youngest sister.

They made her work very hard and wear
ugly old dresses. At night when she had
no more work to do, they made her sit
in the corner in the cinders. That was why
everyone called her Cinderella.

It happened that the prince was going to have a wonderful ball on his birthday. The two older sisters were asked to go, and for days they could think of nothing else. They talked about the dancing and the beautiful dresses they would wear.

When the day came, Cinderella helped them get ready for the prince's ball.

"Do you wish you were going, Cinderella?" asked one of the older sisters.

"Don't make fun of me," Cinderella said. "You know I have nothing to wear."

"You are right," said the ugly sister. "Besides, no one at the ball would want to dance with a cinder girl."

After the two sisters left for the ball,
Cinderella sat down and cried.

"Dear Cinderella, why are you crying?"
asked a soft voice. Cinderella looked up
and saw a beautiful fairy.

"I wish—, I wish—," said Cinderella,
and then she could say no more.

"I know," said the kind fairy. "You wish
to go to the ball, and you shall go."

183

Then, right before Cinderella's eyes,
the fairy began to work her magic.

First she turned a great yellow pumpkin
into a handsome gold coach. Then she turned
six gray mice into six beautiful horses and
a fat rat into a fat coachman.

"Now you can ride to the ball," she said.
"Are you pleased?"

Cinderella was pleased until she looked
down at her old dress. "I have nothing that
I can wear to a ball," she said softly.

Even as she talked, her old dress became
a beautiful one of gold. Her shoes turned
into lovely glass slippers.

"Now you are ready, but you must remember
not to stay after twelve," said the fairy.
"Just at twelve, your gold coach will turn
into a pumpkin, and your horses will become
mice again. Everything else will become as
it was before I used my magic."

"Thank you, kind fairy," said Cinderella.
"I shall leave at twelve or before."

185

The prince came out to meet Cinderella,
and he went with her into the ballroom.
As she came in, the people stopped dancing,
and everyone looked at the princess.

The prince could not take his eyes away,
and he danced only with her. At supper,
he ate nothing, for he wished only to look
at Cinderella.

She sat beside her two older sisters
at the table, but they did not know her.
All through supper, she tried to watch
the clock. She must leave at twelve.

All at once the clock began to strike.
It was striking twelve! Cinderella ran out
of the room. The prince ran fast to catch
her, but she got away.

Then the prince saw a little glass slipper
on the steps. "Did a lovely princess come
past here?" he asked the watchmen.

"Only a little cinder girl came running
past," answered the watchmen.

After Cinderella left, she walked slowly
home. In one of her hands she was carrying
a little glass slipper.

The next day the prince said to everyone
that he wanted to find and marry the girl
who could wear the glass slipper.

His men went all over to have princesses
and ladies try on the slipper, but it was
so small that no one could wear it.

Cinderella's two older sisters tried it on,
but they could not wear it. Their feet were
much too big.

"Let me try it on," said Cinderella.

Her sisters only laughed, but the men saw
that she was very beautiful and wanted her
to try it on, too.

"Come on, cinder girl," they said.

A man placed the little glass slipper
on Cinderella's foot. It went on her foot
just as if it had been made for her. Then
she took the other little glass slipper
from her pocket and put it on, too.

All at once the fairy came and turned
Cinderella into a beautiful princess again,
right before her sisters' eyes.

Now Cinderella's sisters became afraid
and wanted her to forgive them. She told
them not to be afraid, for she would love
them always, as she had in the past.

The happy prince had Cinderella brought to the palace. He found her more beautiful than ever and asked her to marry him.

The two of them were married at once. Cinderella was very happy. Her sisters were happy, too, because she asked them to live in the palace with her.

You see, Cinderella was still as good as she was beautiful.

ACKNOWLEDGMENTS

Grateful credit is given to the following authors and publishers for permission to use copyrighted materials:

Diane Allyn for "The Sky Pony"; Barbee Oliver Carleton for "Valentines for L-L" which appeared under the title "Linda-Lou and Lorelei-Lee" in *Highlights for Children;* Phoebe Cary for "He Didn't Think"; Connie Clayton for "The Magic Bubble"; Frances Darby for "Mike's Halloween Pumpkin" which appeared under the title "Pumpkin-Squash" in *Humpty Dumpty's Magazine;* Lois Davis for "Guess What Day" which appeared in *Grade Teacher;* Mary Jane Fowler for "A Little Bear Takes a Walk" and for "The Bus with the Funny Name"; Anne Guy for "Santa Claus on the Moon" which appeared under the title "Reindeer Mystery" in *The Instructor;* Kathryn Hitte for "Elfred Gets Busy" which appeared under the title "Stick-in-the-Mud" in *Humpty Dumpty's Magazine; Humpty Dumpty's Magazine* for "Mr. Jackson, Mailman" by Nancy Coy and for "Mr. Pickle's Surprise" by Dick and Don Pinnell; Penny Janes for "A Terrible Taxi Ride"; Jane W. Krows for "What You Do" which appeared in *The Instructor;* Edward Lear for "There Was an Old Man"; Lilian Moore for "A Fish Story" which appeared in *Humpty Dumpty's Magazine;* Ilo Orleans for "The Merry Chase" which appeared originally in *The Instructor,* reprinted with permission of the author; Miriam Clark Potter for "Easter Bunny's Big Night" which appeared under the title "Easter Bunny's Accident" in *Humpty Dumpty's Magazine;* Rand McNally & Company for "Mr. Punnymoon's Train" adapted from the book *Mr. Punnymoon's Train* by Alice Hadsell, copyright 1951 by Rand McNally & Company; John Lyle Shimek for "Ya-Hoo for Pancho" adapted from "How Neal Won a New Saddle" which appeared in *Humpty Dumpty's Magazine;* Robert Louis Stevenson for "At the Seaside" from *A Child's Garden of Verses,* published by

Charles Scribner's Sons; The Viking Press, Inc. for "My Dog" from *In and Out* by Tom Robinson, copyright 1943 by Tom Robinson, reprinted by permission of The Viking Press, Inc.; Shirley C. Walker for "Locked in the Supermarket" which appeared in *Jack and Jill*, reprinted by special permission from *Jack and Jill*, copyright 1954, The Curtis Publishing Company; Gertrude Chandler Warner for "The Man and His Goose" which appeared under the title "The Man Who Made a Goose of Himself" in *Child Life;* Gracye Dodge White for "Just a Minute" which appeared under the title "The Minute Story" in *Jack and Jill*, reprinted by special permission from *Jack and Jill*, copyright 1951, The Curtis Publishing Company; Annette Wynne for "Fairy Shoes" which appeared in *Youth's Companion;* Yale University Press for "Bundles" from *Songs for Parents* by John Farrar.

Appreciative credit is given C. B. Ulery, Managing Editor, and Elfrieda L. Schmidt, Associate Editor, for editorial guidance in the selection and presentation of the content of the volume.

Further credit is given William C. Heckler, Art Director, for his effective creative efforts in directing the preparation of art materials for the volume, and to the following artists who created the artwork found on the page numbers accompanying their names: Joseph Giordano, Cover, pages 1, 4, and 5, and pages 121 through 154; Jackie Lacy, end papers and page 6; Kelly Oechsli, pages 2, 3, 22, and 40, pages 105 through 120, pages 155 through 162, and page 173; Bogdan Grom, page 7, pages 8 through 13, and pages 23 through 39; David Stone, pages 14 through 21; Lorence Bjorklund, pages 41 through 58; Henry Picken, pages 59 through 74; Tom O'Sullivan, pages 75 through 104; Robert J. Lee, pages 163, 164, and 180; Marjorie Auerbach, pages 165 through 172; Mel Hunter, pages 174 through 179; Laura Jean Allen, pages 181 through 190.